Footprints iN the Butter

and other mysteries,
riddles and puzzles

Compiled by Pie Corbett
Illustrated by Eleanor Taylor

Belitha Press

Contents

Footprints in the Butter

and other mysteries, riddles and puzzles

To Poppy, who likes
the mystery of the word

First published in Great Britain in 2002 by

Belitha Press
A member of Chrysalis Books plc
64 Brewery Road, London N7 9NT

Series editors: Pie Corbett, Mary-Jane Wilkins
Editor: Russell Mclean
Designer: Sarah Goodwin

ISBN 1 84138 260 4 (hardback)
ISBN 1 84138 262 0 (paperback)

British Library Cataloguing in Publication Data
for this book is available from the British Library.

Printed by Omnia Books Ltd, Glasgow

10 9 8 7 6 5 4 3 2 1 (hb)
10 9 8 7 6 5 4 3 2 1 (pb)

PUZZLES

MYSTERIES

Footprints in the Butter

A rustle in the darkness,
a whisper on the stair,
a message left in code,
and a strand of golden hair.

Trapped inside a mystery,
high notes from a fiddle.
Heart beats beat much faster –
the answer is a riddle.

A sudden crash at midnight
made the girl's heart flutter.
She looked inside the fridge –
saw footprints in the butter.

Detectives are all baffled
by this tissue made of lies.
The only clue they've found
is hidden from their eyes.

The footprints have them baffled.
how could anything survive –
trapped inside the fridge
where nothing is alive?

So, nothing is the answer.
The proof is plain to see.
The riddle hides the truth
locked inside the mystery.

Pie Corbett

Counting Steps

Going down
To breakfast
I counted
Thirteen steps
On the stairs.

Coming up
To bed
I counted
Fourteen steps.

Now I'm in bed
And worried.
Where did
The extra step
Come from?

Everyone is asleep.
I creep on to the landing.
I count the steps again.

Twelve.

Roger Stevens

I AM

I am the tree that holds up the sky,
I am the question asking why?
I am the ocean that laps the land,
I am the tide that smooths the sand,
I am the bird that greets the dawn,
I am the lost one all forlorn.
I am the sun that lights the earth,
I am the friend that knows your worth,
I am the faith that keeps you going,
I am the mind that insists on knowing,
I am the night that brings you sleep,
I am the dream that goes down deep.

John Cotton

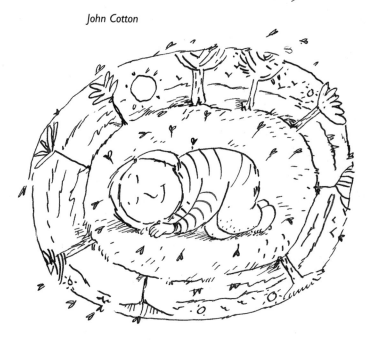

The Woodsman and the Green Children

(Forest of Dean, 1857)

Masked by the forest's leafy screen
a Woodsman saw the strangest scene.
He gazed upon a dappled glade
and watched two children, coloured green.

He watched as on all fours they played
and loped like wolves from light to shade.
Amazed at how they snarled and yowled,
hid in the holt the Woodsman stayed.

Then came a she-wolf, sharp-fang jowled.
Into the dappled glade she prowled.
The Woodsman saw the children quail,
then run towards her when she growled.

The poor man felt his courage fail
and, as the two green children howled,
he hastened down the forest trail,
returned to town and told this tale,
   returned to town and told this tale.

Wes Magee

WiLderNeSS

Miss says wilderness
is beautiful, natural, endless...
is space.

Mum's Oxford English Dictionary states:
'wild or uncultivated land'.

At the end of our garden
there's a lime tree.
I climb it, high as I can.

Sometimes
I sit up there for hours,
especially in the dark,
staring at the stars,
touching wilderness,

out there
and inside me.

Joan Poulson

MiNOU

A sky-blue cat leapt at nothing on the lawn.
Her paws caught air.
Her jaws snapped shut on the scent of roses.
Sunlight poured through her.
She left no shadow to run beneath her.
Tail up, she brought her catch to me,
laid the undamaged perfume at my feet.
I breathed it in, heard her ecstatic purr.
My lap hollowed.
I felt the warmth of her weightless ghost.

Catherine Benson

Goodwin Sands

I have seen the pale gulls circle
against a restless sky;
I have heard the dark winds crying
as dusk-drawn clouds wheel by.

But the waiting waves still whisper
of shadowy ocean lands,
of twisting tides and of secrets
that lie beneath the Sands.

I have seen the wild weeds' tangle
and smelt the salted squall;
I have seen the moon rise from the seas,
and felt the long night's fall.

But whose are the voices that echo
from the shifting ocean lands,
that tell of secrets buried
beneath the drifting Sands?

For many sail the Goodwins
and some return to shore;
but others ride in the falling tide
and those are seen no more.

And voices rise from the waters
beneath a restless sky:
in the dying light of coming night
the long-lost sailors sigh;
from the watery lands of Goodwin Sands
I hear the sailors cry.

Judith Nicholls

The Myth of Creation

A dragon flew out of the sun
and from its flames whole worlds were spun
and from its names were words begun
with all we've thought and said and done
and wars were fought and lost and won
and tales were taught and lies were spun
that a dragon flew out of the sun.

Nick Toczek

A Crowd of Crows

A crowd of crows
perched by the road
on top of a tall oak tree.
A crowd of crows
perched by the road,
and here's what they said to me:

'You will see the world
as a jewel-eyed toad
when you turn the burning key;

'You will feel the weight
of the thistledown's load
before you float wild and free.'

Dave Ward

The Rainbow Mystery

One minute it was raining,
the sun had just peeked through,
and all things were as normal
when out of the grey and blue

this great big coloured arch
leapt into the sky
several miles wide, I guess,
and pretty near as high

and stood without permission,
over council land,
an unofficial structure
of the kind that we had banned.

No one had sought approval
or put in an application,
it was clearly a cowboy job
with ideas above its station.

And then it went clean missing
leaving nothing in its place
and the company that built it
is proving hard to trace.

George Szirtes

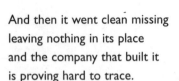

RIDDLES

Turn to page 61 to find the answers to these riddles.

SOUNDS OF SILENCE?

My words fill your head
like a chattering tongue,
though I'm as mute as a marble,
silent as stone.

I cheer you or sadden,
puzzle or preach;
entertain you, persuade you,
amuse you or teach.

Paperweight, motionless,
soundless as bone...
yet though speechless,
not spineless: I carry
a weight of my own.

Choose me now, use me,
then set me down:
never fear, I'll be there

when you are long gone!

Judith Nicholls

WHO AM I?

I'm not made of jelly
and I'm not a fish,
so don't try to eat me
with chips in a dish.

And speaking of jelly,
I'm not fit to eat
with ice cream or custard
as your special treat.

But one thing is certain,
when you're at the beach
be careful when swimming,
stay out of my reach.

I bristle with danger
in poisonous stings.
And I'm on the lookout
for edible things.

Brian D'Arcy

GUESS

I've studied studs
and withstood studs
as they have stood on me,

been bald and burnt
and mashed in mud
and wet and slippery,

been sewn as seed
and seen as sod
and rolled repeatedly,

and often mown
as I have grown.
Whatever can I be?

Gina Douthwaite

In the Woods

A closed pale fist in the dark,
greening fingers groping for light,
blue heads ring in the spring.

Catherine Benson

What am I?

I am light as a breeze,
a puff of pink smoke;
a chin-sticker, lip-gripper,
fluffy pink joke!

I cling to your fingers,
I curl round your thumb;
then like a small duvet
I wrap round your tongue.

Judith Nicholls

Water in Disguise

Water in disguise:
Three answers (no prize!)
This water's a stick;
This water's a star;
This water's so thick
You're not sure where you are.

Eric Finney

Fathers and Sons

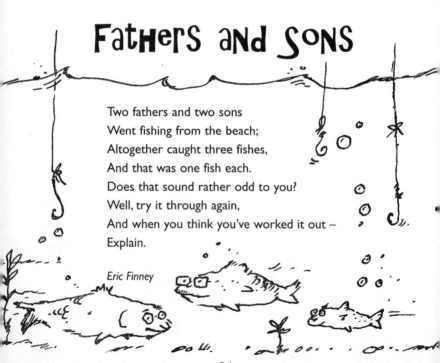

Two fathers and two sons
Went fishing from the beach;
Altogether caught three fishes,
And that was one fish each.
Does that sound rather odd to you?
Well, try it through again,
And when you think you've worked it out –
Explain.

Eric Finney

One Boy

Teddy, Eddie, Neddy and Ted
Woke from their slumbers, jumped out of bed,
Played in the sunshine, swam in the sea,
Laughed in the wind, ran home to tea.
But when the day ended, strange as it seems,
Only one boy lay down to sweet dreams.
What was his name?

Jennifer Curry

Night Hunter

Some think that I am blind by day.
At night my sharp eyes seek out prey.
I haunt the woodlands with my song.
I'm wise. And smaller creatures know I'm strong.
Who? Who am I?

John Kitching

AN Artist

He painted cornfields, starry skies,
the weariness in peasants' eyes.
He painted orchards in full bloom,
the reaper and the weaver's loom.
He painted sunflowers, bold and bright,
his lonely room, the Rhone at night.
His mind was tortured. Though his art
came from his soul it broke his heart.

Marian Swinger

ONe Tree

From one tree you might make
A million of these;
Yet one could destroy
A million trees.

Eric Finney

WHat is it?

It's after the asking,
It's nearly a noose,
It's a crook,
It's a hook
With a blob that's come loose.

Eric Finney

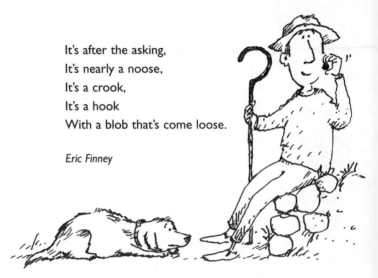

Head With a Tail

Head with a tail,
Each day plumper,
On the way
From jelly to jumper.

Eric Finney

Summer Surprise

My first is in shell but not in tree.
My second is in spell and also in three.
My third is in land but not in tide.
My fourth is in stand and also in side.
My fifth is in ice-pop but not in cone.
My sixth is in dew-drop but not in stone.
My seventh is in bucket and also in spade.
My whole is somewhere to paddle and wade.

Janis Priestley

RiddLe

My first is in fish but not in chip.
My second in teeth but not in lip.
My third's in potato but not in plum.
My fourth's in mouth and also in thumb.
My fifth is in pear but not in cherry.
My sixth is in bacon but not in berry.
My last is in chocolate but not in crumble.
Sometimes when I'm empty you'll hear me rumble.

John Foster

AN Egyptian Riddle

My first is in face but not in head
My second is in needle but not in thread
My third is in beauty but not in tan
My fourth is in woman but not in man
My fifth is in pearls but not in stone
My sixth is in monarch but not in throne
My seventh is in Egypt but not in Greece
My eighth is in war but not in peace
My last is in snake but not in strike
Who am I? Guess if you like.

Marcus Moore

HiddeN Secrets

know m ^{oreabou} tyoutha_n
I you think: what you
like to eat and like
to drink; what you
wear, where you've
been, sometimes,
where you're going
– don't worry, I'll
keep a lid on things.

Mike Johnson

Riddle Me Re

Not a horse, but has a saddle,
Not a ram, but has a horn,
Not a writer, but makes her mark
What was the name with which she was born?

*Albanian riddle translated by Elona Velca
and Andrew Fusek Peters*

There Stands an Oak

There stands an oak
And from that oak,
twelve branches grew,
And on each branch,
nests two plus two
And in each nest,
seven eggs bright blue.

*Czech riddle translated
by Andrew Fusek Peters*

A Game of Chance

RattLesnake, Boomslang,
CobrA, Boa, Taipan,
DiamonD Back, Copperhead,
Upside-Down snake playing dead.
SnakEs that crush, snakes that bite,
HungRy snakes with appetites,
AdderS, Pythons, Fer-de-Lance,
Roll the dice and take a chance.

Jane Clarke

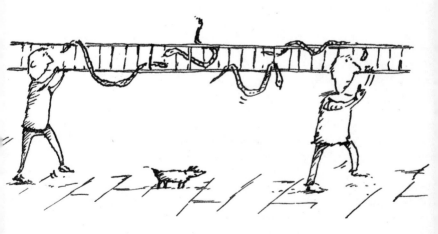

Haiku

In darkness I hide
The weight of the world upon
My tireless shoulders

When found I am thrown
Into the flaming furnace
And my soul's set free

Roger Stevens

Come a Riddle

Come a riddle, come a riddle,
come a rin-din-din,
   blue blood runs down a body so thin,
   it tells a story without ever a grin,
come a riddle, come a riddle,
come a rin-din-din.

Come a riddle, come a riddle,
come a rin-din-rood,
   black bone runs through a circle of wood,
   it tells a story no tongue ever could,
come a riddle, come a riddle,
come a rin-din-rood.

John Rice

GoodNight

The click of a switch.
In his glass bowl the gold snake
is at once asleep.

Pamela Gillilan

You and I

I am you
And you are me.
Reflect, my friend,
On this mystery.

John Kitching

Flight Path

I need no calendar:
> one day in late Summer,
>> something in the light tilts;
>>> the weather speaks deep
>>>> in my blood and feathers,
>>>>> tells me it's time to go.

>>>>> I need no map, no lodestar:
>>>> the route home is printed
>>> here in my curved wings;
>> my flight is urgent, slanted
> free as the trade winds

singing *Africa, Africa.*

Tony Charles

The Watcher

Stands where fish are, dragged with sunlight
or holding still on dark reeds, waiting;
he knows them.

Speed is in his eye, and the image
of that which would be killed;
he makes no bargains.

Strength is in his wings, the wide sweep
lifting him into the astonished air, so big.
He takes where he chooses from the shallows.

What lives here, all of it is his.
Older than legend, the grey king struts
arrogant over the white lake.

Tony Charles

Change is My Business

Change is my business;
That which is hardest, I eat:
Sword-blade, axe-head, horse-shoe, nail.
Wheels turn, but my hunger is steadfast.
Time and cold rain are my henchmen.
When a man says, 'This is made for ever,'
I gnash my teeth and laugh.

Tony Charles

Shape-Shifter

Shape-shifter, smooth skinned
Death-bringer, sharp as wind;
Sidetracker across soft sands;
Subtle swimmer in silent seas;
Prey-seizer without hands,
Sinuous climber of tall trees.

Tony Charles

Seven Wonders

Painted glass bauble,
swung on an unseen thread.

Curled palette of light,
splashed on dark canvas.

Lapis lazuli,
brush-stroked with white.

Lone marble,
rolled over threadbare velvet.

A medal,
pinned to the blue blazer of night.

Space-hopper,
cast like a kite over silent seas.

Small change
in a deep pocket.

Judith Nicholls

WHite SNaKe

I saw a white snake
Leave its tunnel
To lie on a bed of spikes
And enter a man's mouth,
Making him spit and froth.

Yet it was he
Who opened his lips
To receive the snake.

Gerard Benson

CRYSTAL ZOO

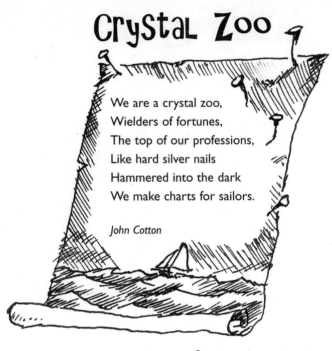

We are a crystal zoo,
Wielders of fortunes,
The top of our professions,
Like hard silver nails
Hammered into the dark
We make charts for sailors.

John Cotton

SiLENT...

Silent I invade cities,
Blur edges, confuse travellers,
My thumb smudging the light.
I drift from rivers
To loiter in early morning fields,
Until constable sun
Moves me on.

John Cotton

A Watery Riddle

Vain as I almost am, I can act
Any part that requires tears:
When really turning on the tap
I decorate whole fields with mirrors,
The mirrors with a hundred glittering rings.

Lawrence Sail

Hello

I am the two-knuckled bone
That joins your tongue and ear.
To be close to me is to know
The secret of defeating distance.
Hold me! Speak to me! Listen!
For every word that you give me
I will repay you with others.

Lawrence Sail

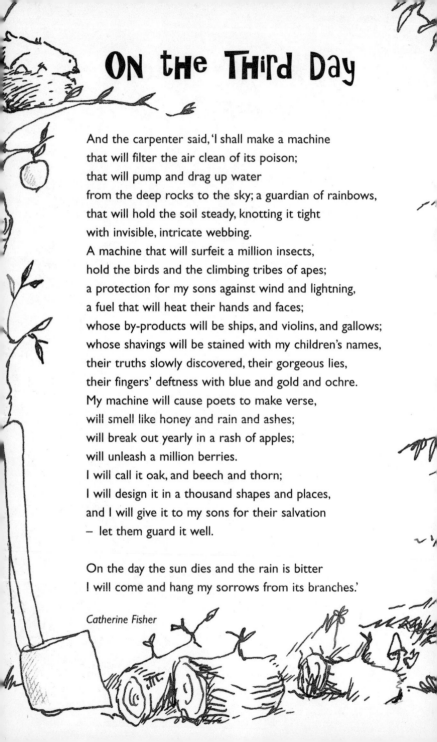

On the Third Day

And the carpenter said, 'I shall make a machine
that will filter the air clean of its poison;
that will pump and drag up water
from the deep rocks to the sky; a guardian of rainbows,
that will hold the soil steady, knotting it tight
with invisible, intricate webbing.
A machine that will surfeit a million insects,
hold the birds and the climbing tribes of apes;
a protection for my sons against wind and lightning,
a fuel that will heat their hands and faces;
whose by-products will be ships, and violins, and gallows;
whose shavings will be stained with my children's names,
their truths slowly discovered, their gorgeous lies,
their fingers' deftness with blue and gold and ochre.
My machine will cause poets to make verse,
will smell like honey and rain and ashes;
will break out yearly in a rash of apples;
will unleash a million berries.
I will call it oak, and beech and thorn;
I will design it in a thousand shapes and places,
and I will give it to my sons for their salvation
– let them guard it well.

On the day the sun dies and the rain is bitter
I will come and hang my sorrows from its branches.'

Catherine Fisher

Would Not Saw

I would not saw the wood I see
if what I saw was still a tree.

Selima Hill

Light as a Light

Light as a light
and tall as a house,
the colour of angels,
the squeak of a mouse.

Selima Hill

Take a Field

Take a field. Dry it. Mill it.
Add a belly. Warm it. Fill it.

Selima Hill

White Fence

White fence, pink hill,
black valley, ruined mill.

Selima Hill

PUZZLES

LONDON A-Z

Zealous young xylophonists wait vacantly
under thundery skies,
rarely quiet,
playing on,
nightly.

Melodies lurk knowingly,
jingle, invade hearts,
glide from each deep corner,
begging answers.

Judith Nicholls

ALieN NurSery RHyMe

Eydid aldid al
Dick aton di fidel di
Kowjum petoffer di
Moooon

Di liddled oglaft
Ooosie suijfunnan didi
Shran awaiwiff di
Sboooon

Translated by Roger Stevens

SHOEM*

Time flizzes when I'm wrizzing –
some words are toomely long,
and so I merge and jummix
to squeet them in my song.

It's really not too diffcky
to get my words to scrush –
saves tromoil and timassle,
when in a hurrid rush.

There's only one small difflem
for my puzzizzy head –
I'm baffplussed and conboozled
by what it is I said!

Liz Brownlee

50

*Short Poem

flizzes = flies and whizzes
wrizzing = busy and writing
toomely = too and extremely
jummix = jumble and mix
squeet = squeeze and fit
diffcky = difficult and tricky
scrush = squash and crush
tromoil = trouble and turmoil
timassle = time and hassle
hurrid = hurried and horrid
difflem = difficulty and problem
puzzizzy = puzzled and dizzy
baffplussed = baffled and nonplussed
conboozled = confused and bamboozled

ContrariWise

How wise is contrary?
As wise as a clock?
How hardy is a fool?
How sure is a cock?

Acting as nuts as dough,
feeling as free as care,
stay as loose as a foot
and as tight as air.

You start proud as a house
and as strong as a head,
end up soiled as a shop
and as locked as dead.

Jokes as sick as the sea
leave you stained as a tear.
Luck as sore as a cold
leaves you marked as an ear.

Though you're bitten as frost
and as struck as thunder,
as eaten as a moth
and as ground as under,

though you're blind as snow
and as bald as a pie,
as forsaken as God,
just think... contrariwise

and life's as full as wonder.

Philip Gross

Mr Bird

Nobody liked Mr Bird.
He could tern nasty,
Couldn't keep his heron,
Always bittern and twisted.
When he hawked his wares on doorsteps
Had to buzzard on the doorbell,
Duck when stuff was chucked at him.
Richard was always ravenous,
Would swallow down
A bowl of corncrakes whole
And something on a skua,
But his grebe was such
He fell to robin passers-by,
Made all his victims quail.
A chase ensued one day, then he ran out of petrel.
Spent the nightingale.
The neighbours were so choughed
Then ran to fetch the bunting when they heard
And fixed it with a yellowhammer,
Thinking 'Ah, how pheasant life can be
Without that Dicky Bird!'

Sue Cowling

54

Deer Reed

This poem is a univocalic — a poem which uses only one vowel.

Three deer tremble by the September elms
Where scree defends tree.
Reeds jerk where the creek ebbs.

Here the kestrel queen preens herself:
She reflects the fever screech event —
never seeks her sweet shell eye-sleep.

John Rice

THe PaliNdroMeS

Mr and Mrs Palindrome
Live in a house on a hill:
There's Mum and Dad
And Nan and Bob
And Anna and Eve and Lil.
There's Otto the dog
And Pip the pup
And black cats Viv and Ziz:
There's something strange
About their names...
I wonder what it is?

Eric Finney

TWo ANagriddLes

The one-word solution to each riddle is also an anagram of the words in **bold** type.

Docile? Cor!
You must be joking!
His jaws are
Positively smoking!

Eric Finney

Like a newt
This one may seem.
It lived in fire
In **Alan's dream.**

Eric Finney

SHiFTiNG SPeLLS

Anger
Quickly
Shifts to danger.
Happy chance
Can quickly
Change
That danger
Into
Dancer.
A little shaft
Of spell can spill
A question
Into answer.

John Kitching

Have You Read?

Enjoy Your Homework	by R.U. Joking
Out for the Count	by I.C. Stars
Cliff-Top Rescue	by Justin Time
A Year in Space	by Esau Mars
Your Turn to Wash Up	by Y. Mee
Off to the Dentist	by U. First
Broken Windows	by E. Dunnett
Pickpocket Pete	by M.T. Purse
Lions on the Loose	by Luke Out
Helping Gran	by B.A. Dear
Ten Ice Creams	by Segovia Flaw
Rock Concert	by Q. Here

Judith Nicholls

THe CHaMeLeoN

treetreetreetreetreetree
treetreetreetreetreetreetreetree
treetreetreetreetreetreetreetreetreetree
treetreetreetreetreetreetreetreetreetreetree
treetreetreetreetreetreetreetreetreetreetreetree
treetreetreetreetreetreetreetreetreetreetreetreetree
treetreetreetreeyoutreecantreesearchtreealltreedaytreetreetree
treetreetreetreetreetreetreetreetreetreetreetreetreetreetree
treetreetreetreebuttreetreetreeyou'lltreenevertreeseetreetreetreetree
treetreetreetreetreetreereetreetreetreetreetreetreereetreetreetree
treetreetreetreetreetreetreetreetreetreetreetreetreetreetreetreetree
treetreetreetreetreetreetreetreethetreechameleontreehidingtreetreetree
treetreetreetreetreetreetreetreetreetreetreetreetreetreetreetree
treetreetreetreeintreethetreetreetreetreetreetreetreetreetreetree
treetreetreetreetreetreetreetreetreetreetreetreetreetreetree
treetreetreetreetreetreetreetreetreetreetreetree
treetreetreetreetreetreetreetreetreetree
treetreetreetreetreetreetreetree
treetreetreetreetreetree
treetreetreetreetree
treetreetreetree
treetreetreet
treetreetree
treetreetree
treetreetree
treetreetree
treetreetree
treetreetree
treetreetree

Roger Stevens

ANSWeRS to RiddLeS

Index of Titles and First Lines

First lines are in italics

INdeX oF AutHors

AcKNoWLedgeMents

Catherine Benson: 'Minou' and 'In the Woods' © Catherine Benson. **Gerard Benson**: 'White Snake' © Gerard Benson, first published in *In Wordsworth's Chair* (Flambard Press, 1995). **Liz Brownlee**: 'Shoem' © Liz Brownlee. **Tony Charles**: 'Flight Path', The Watcher' and 'Change is my Business' © Tony Charles. **Jane Clarke**: 'A Game of Chance' © Jane Clarke. **Pie Corbett**: 'Footprints in the Butter' © Pie Corbett. **John Cotton**: 'I Am' © John Cotton, first published in *The Ammonite's Revenge* (Tricky Sam), 'Crystal Zoo' and 'Silent' © John Cotton, first published in *The Crystal Zoo* (OUP). **Sue Cowling**: 'Mr Bird' © Sue Cowling. **Jennifer Curry**: 'One Boy' © Jennifer Curry. **Brian D'Arcy**: 'Who Am I?' © Brian D'Arcy. **Gina Douthwaite**: 'Guess' © Gina Douthwaite. **Eric Finney**: 'Water in Disguise', Fathers and Sons', 'One Tree', 'What is it?', 'The Palindromes' and 'Two Anagriddles' © Eric Finney. **Catherine Fisher**: 'On the Third Day' © Catherine Fisher. **John Foster**: 'Riddle' © John Foster. **Andrew Fusek Peters**: 'Riddle Me Re' and 'There Stands an Oak' © Andrew Fusek Peters, first published in *Sheep Don't Go to School* (Bloodaxe, 1999). **Pamela Gillilan**: 'Goodnight' © Pamela Gillilan. **Philip Gross**: 'Contrariwise' © Philip Gross. **Selima Hill**: 'Would not Saw', 'Light as a Light', 'Take a Field' and 'White Fence' © Selima Hill, originally commissioned by the Science Museum, London. **Mike Johnson**: 'Hidden Secrets' © Mike Johnson. **John Kitching**: 'Night Hunter', 'You and I' and 'Shifting Spells' © John Kitching. **Wes Magee**: 'The Woodsman and the Green Children' © Wes Magee, first published in *The Phantom's Fang-tastic Show* (OUP, 2000). **Marcus Moore**: 'An Egyptian Riddle' © Marcus Moore. **Judith Nicholls**: 'Goodwin Sands' © Judith Nicholls, first published in *Storm's Eye* (OUP 1994), 'Sounds of Silence', 'What Am I?', 'Seven Wonders' © Judith Nicholls, first published in *The Earth Does Not Belong to Man* (Longman, 2000), 'London A-Z' and 'Have You Read? © Judith Nicholls. **Joan Poulson**: 'Wilderness' © Joan Poulson. **Janis Priestley**: 'Summer Surprise' © Janis Priestley. **John Rice**: 'Come a Riddle' and 'Deer Reed' © John Rice. **Lawrence Sail**: 'A Watery Riddle' and 'Hello' © Lawrence Sail. **Roger Stevens**: 'Counting Steps', 'Haiku' and 'Alien Nursery Rhyme' © Roger Stevens, 'The Chameleon', © Roger Stevens, first published in *The Upside Down Frown* (Wayland, 1999). **Marian Swinger**: 'An Artist' © Marian Swinger. **George Szirtes**: 'The Rainbow Mystery' © George Szirtes. **Nick Toczek**: 'The Myth of Creation' © Nick Toczek. **Elona Velca**: 'Riddle Me Re' © Elona Velca, first published in *Sheep Don't Go to School* (Bloodaxe, 1999). **Dave Ward**: 'A Crowd of Crows' © Dave Ward.

Every effort has been made to contact copyright holders. The publishers would like to hear from any copyright holder not acknowledged.